Curious George
Curious About
LETTERS

www.hmhbooks.com
www.curiousgeorge.com
ISBN: 978-0-547-47281-2
Manufactured in China
LEO 10 9 8 7 6 5 4 3 2 1
4500338239

Houghton Mifflin Harcourt
Boston   New York   2012

Aa

A is the beginning of the alphabet.

George is curious about these objects. They are words that all begin with A, except for one. Cross it out!

Practice writing your uppercase and lowercase As.

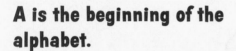

What does George think about when he thinks of the letter B? Circle the person who is not thinking about a word that begins with the letter B.

Practice writing.

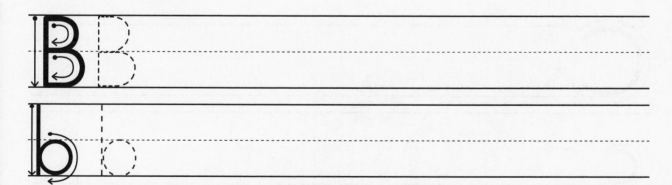

C c

C is one of George's favorite letters because cake begins with C. Help George decorate his cake by adding color.

Practice writing.

C ⌐---

C ⌐---

Cross out all of the letters except D.

D A D B A C D D A
D B A D C D A B C

Circle only the lowercase d's.

d b a d c b d a b c
a c d a b c d c a b

Practice writing.

George is drawing the outline of the letter E. Trace his lines and then color.

Practice writing.

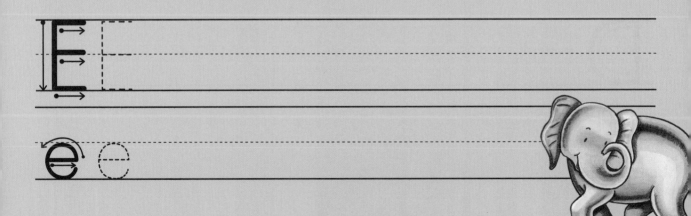

Circle all the things that begin with the letter F. You can color them too.

Practice writing.

G g

Help George find all the animals that begin with G. Circle the ones you find.

Practice writing.

For the letter H, color the uppercase and lowercase letters in red. Use other colors for the rest of the letters.

Practice writing.

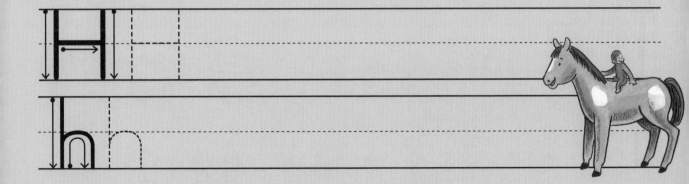

I

George is counting insects. You might also know insects as bugs. Color the insects that crawl on the ground.

Practice writing.

What does the handle of an umbrella have in common with the letter J? That's right—its shape! You can draw the letter J by adding handles to these umbrellas.

Practice writing.

K k

Which animals below have names that begin with the letter K? Circle them and color.

Practice writing.

For the letter L, color the uppercase and lowercase letters blue. Color the other letters different colors if you like.

Practice writing.

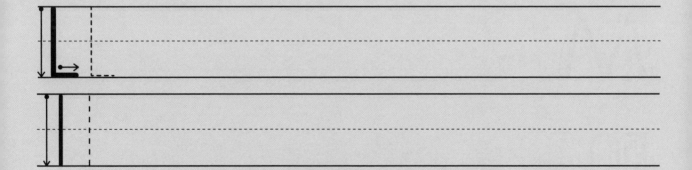

Color the sections labeled with the uppercase letter **M** green, and the shapes with the lowercase **m** orange.

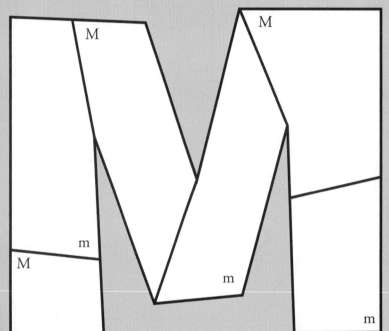

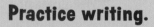

Practice writing.

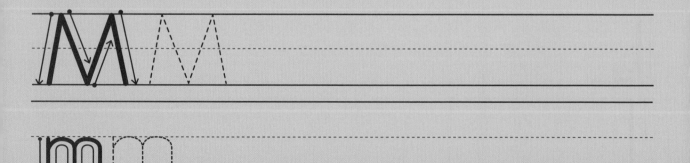

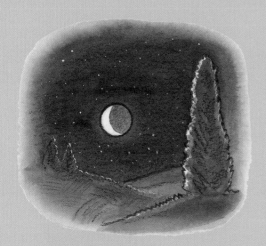

Nn

Connect the dots. What part of the animal did you draw? That's right—his nose!

Practice writing.

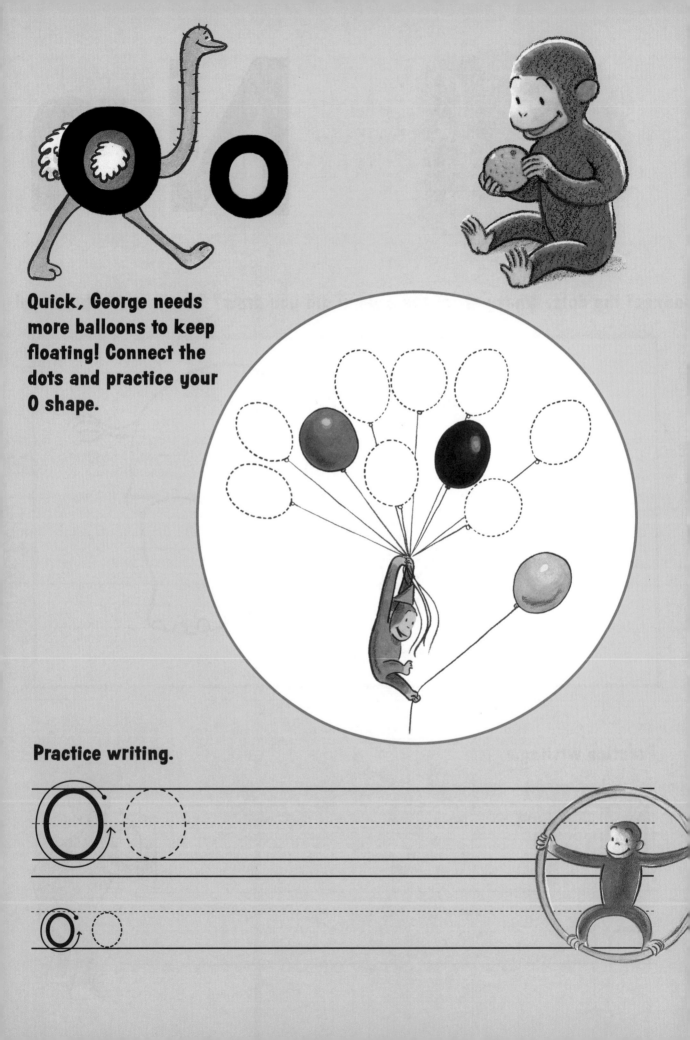

Quick, George needs more balloons to keep floating! Connect the dots and practice your O shape.

Practice writing.

P p

Circle the animals that begin with the letter P.

George is making pizza. Decorate this slice with foods that begin with the letter P.

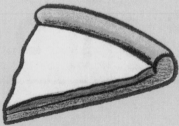

Practice writing.

Cross out all of the letters except Q.

Q P O Q O G Q B O Q P Q

B O P G O D R O Q G O D

V Q X S Q V Q Q X Q S

C O P G U D Q B C O P G

Practice writing.

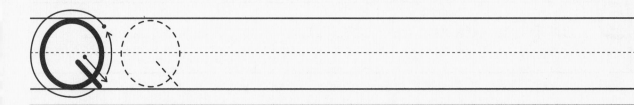

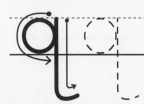

Color all uppercase and lowercase R's purple.

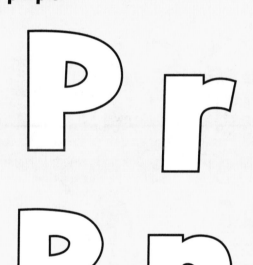

Practice writing.

R R

r r

 **S s**

**Circle the animal whose name begins
with the letter S.**

Practice writing.

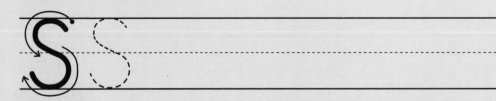

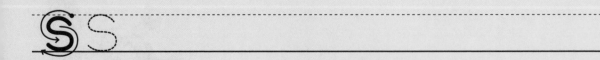

George is spending a day at the farm. Circle the things he sees that begin with the letter T.

Practice writing.

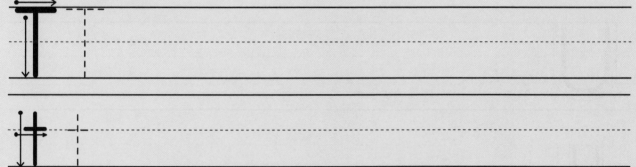

U u

George loves to paint. Help him decorate this wall and practice writing U at the same time!

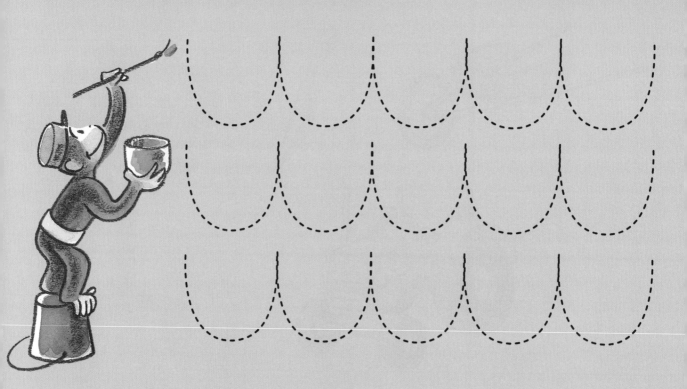

Practice writing.

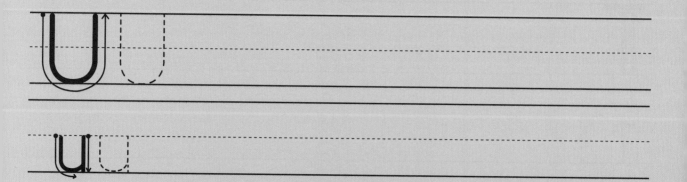

Finish these kites for George to fly. You'll be practicing your letter V at the same time!

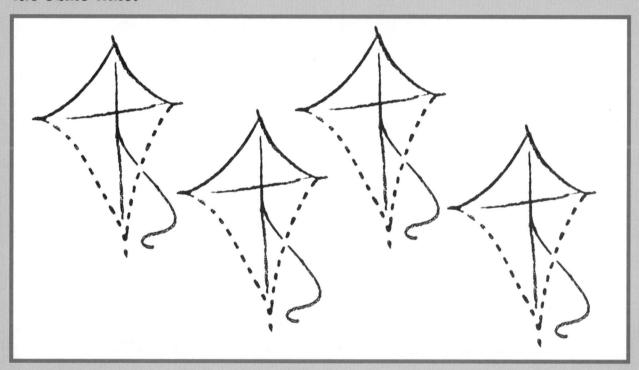

Practice writing.

Circle the season that begins with the letter W.

Practice writing.

W w

W w

Help the baby animals find their mother. You'll be practicing your letter X at the same time!

Practice writing.

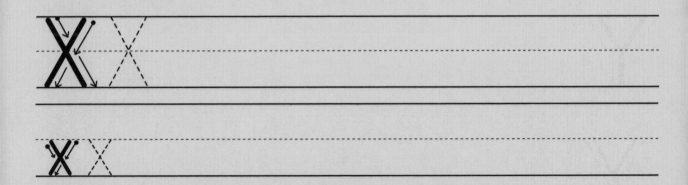

Cross out all of the letters except Y.

Y U V U Y V

Y U Y V V U Y

Practice writing.

Z z

Cross out the animal you would not find at the zoo.
Circle the animal whose name begins with the letter Z.

Practice writing.

Z

Z

Draw a line between the uppercase and lowercase versions of each letter.

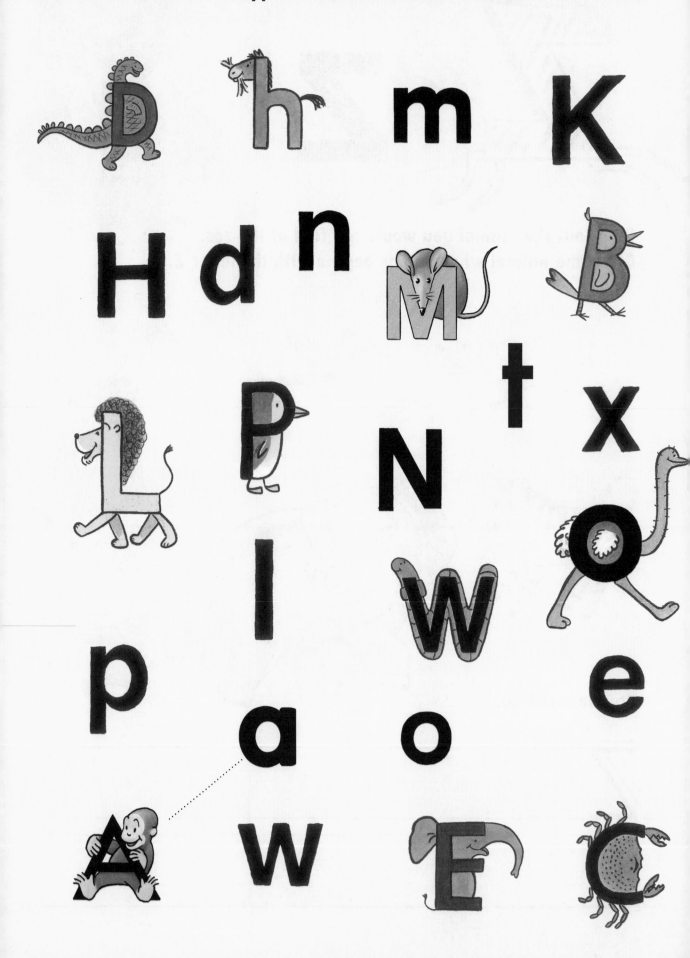

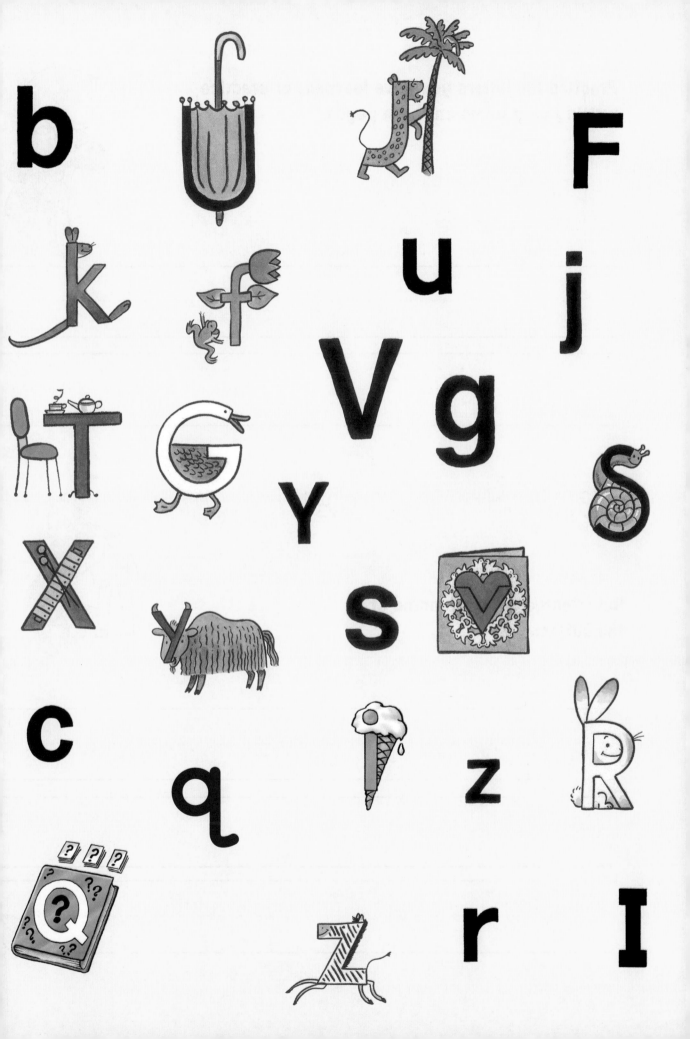

Practice the letters you have learned, or practice writing your name on these pages.

_____

- - - - - - - - - - - - - - - -

_____

- - - - - - - - - - - - - - - -

_____

Help George write his name at the bottom.

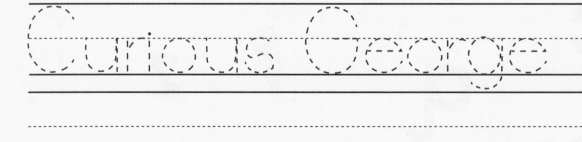

_____

- - - - - - - - - - - - - - - -

_____

- - - - - - - - - - - - - - - -

_____